D1401493

To my children,
Mary, Laura, and Gregory,
for their love and understanding,
and for memories of Christmas past
and hopes for Christmas future.

ACKNOWLEDGEMENTS

A very merry "thank you" to my friends and members of my family
who posed for the characters found throughout this edition of
A Christmas Treasury.

CAST OF CHARACTERS

Michael Paglia - Santa
Dena Hansen - Mary
Adam Kubert - Joseph
Joseph Scrocco, Jr. - Shepherd
William McGuire - Shepherd
Greg Hildebrandt - Shepherd, King, Sailor
Kevin McGinty - Angel
Alicia DeVincenzi - Child Caroling
Jim McCann - Child Caroling
Heidi Corso - Angel
Vincent Colandrea - Medieval Lord
Jean Scrocco - Medieval Lady
Ron Maver - Squire
Honey Maver - Lady In Waiting
Gene O'Brien - King, Papa ('Twas)
Linda Hanover - Young Lover
Alan Hallerman - Young Lover
Gregory Hildebrandt - Elf
Karen White - Elf
Robbie McCann - Child Sleeping
Annie Green - Child Sleeping

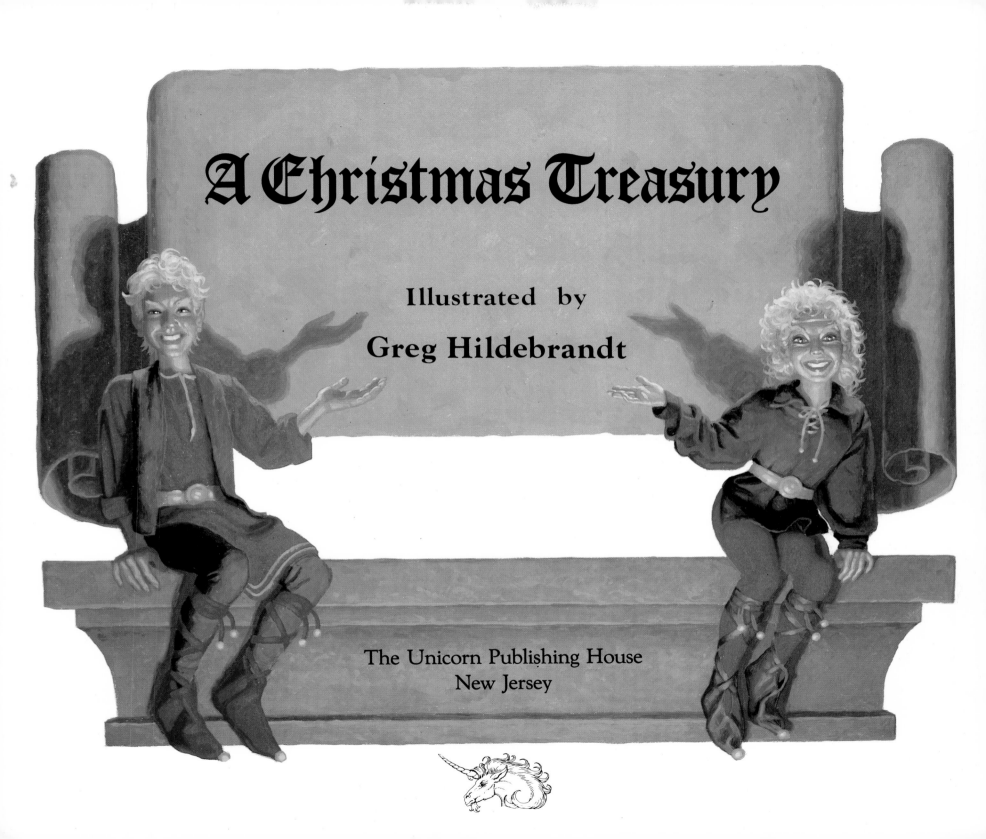

A Christmas Treasury

Illustrated by

Greg Hildebrandt

The Unicorn Publishing House

New Jersey

©1984 The Unicorn Publishing House, Inc., All Rights Reserved
Art Work: © 1984 Greg Hildebrandt, All Rights Reserved
This book may not be reproduced in whole or in part, by any means,
without written permission. For information, contact Jean L. Scrocco at

The Unicorn Publishing House; 1148 Parsippany Blvd.; Parsippany, NJ 07054

Distributed in Canada by Doubleday Canada, Ltd., Toronto, ON, Canada
Distributed in the rest of the world by Columbus Books, Ltd., London, England

◆◆◆◆◆

Designed and Edited by Jean L. Scrocco
Music consultant: Dale Trimmer
Printed in Korea by Sam Seong Publishing & Printing Co., Ltd. through Creative Graphics International Inc., New York, NY
Typography by TG&IF, Inc., Fairfield, NJ
Reproduction photography by The Color Wheel, New York, NY

◆◆◆◆◆

Special thanks to Kate Klimo and Yoh Jinno

◆◆◆◆◆

Printing History 15 14 13 12 11 10 9 8 7 6 5 4 3

Library of Congress Cataloging in Publication Data
Main entry under title:

A Christmas Treasury.

Summary: Includes illustrated versions of eight carols,
the story of the Nativity, and the famous narrative
poem about St. Nicholas' Christmas Eve Visit.

1. Christmas — Literary collections. [1. Christmas —
Literary collections] I. Hildebrandt, Greg, ill.
PZ5.C476 1984349.2'6828284-8798
ISBN 0-88101-017-0.

'Twas The Night Before Christmas

By
C. Clement Moore

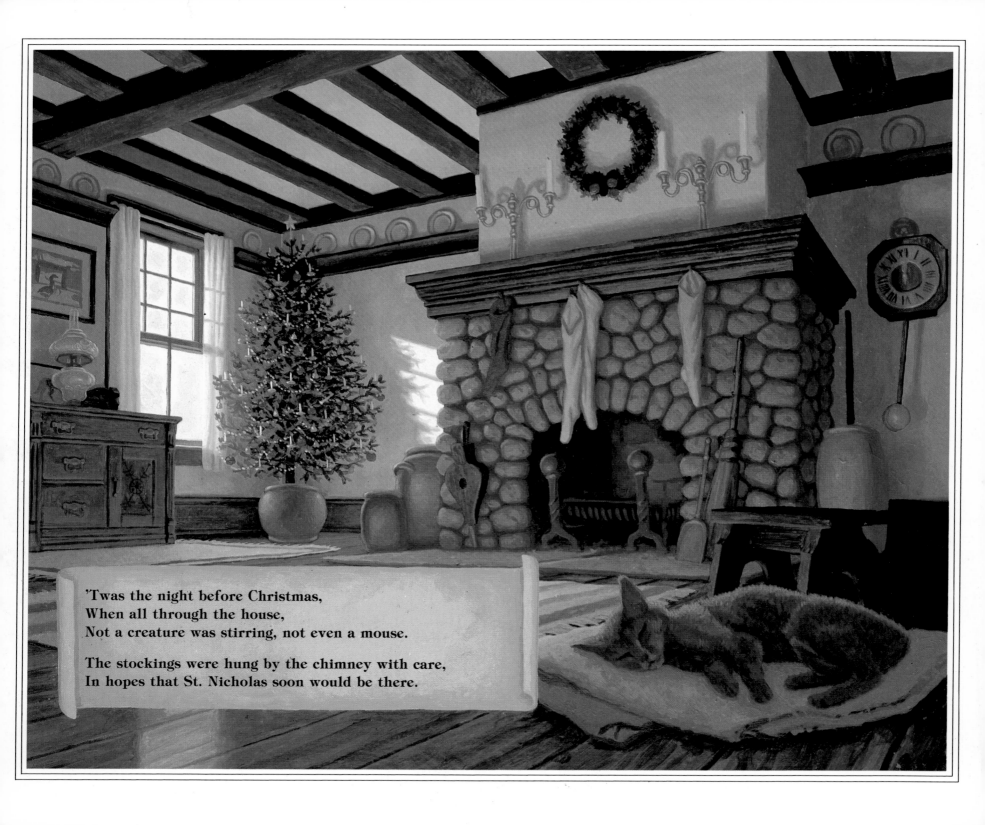

'Twas the night before Christmas,
When all through the house,
Not a creature was stirring, not even a mouse.

The stockings were hung by the chimney with care,
In hopes that St. Nicholas soon would be there.

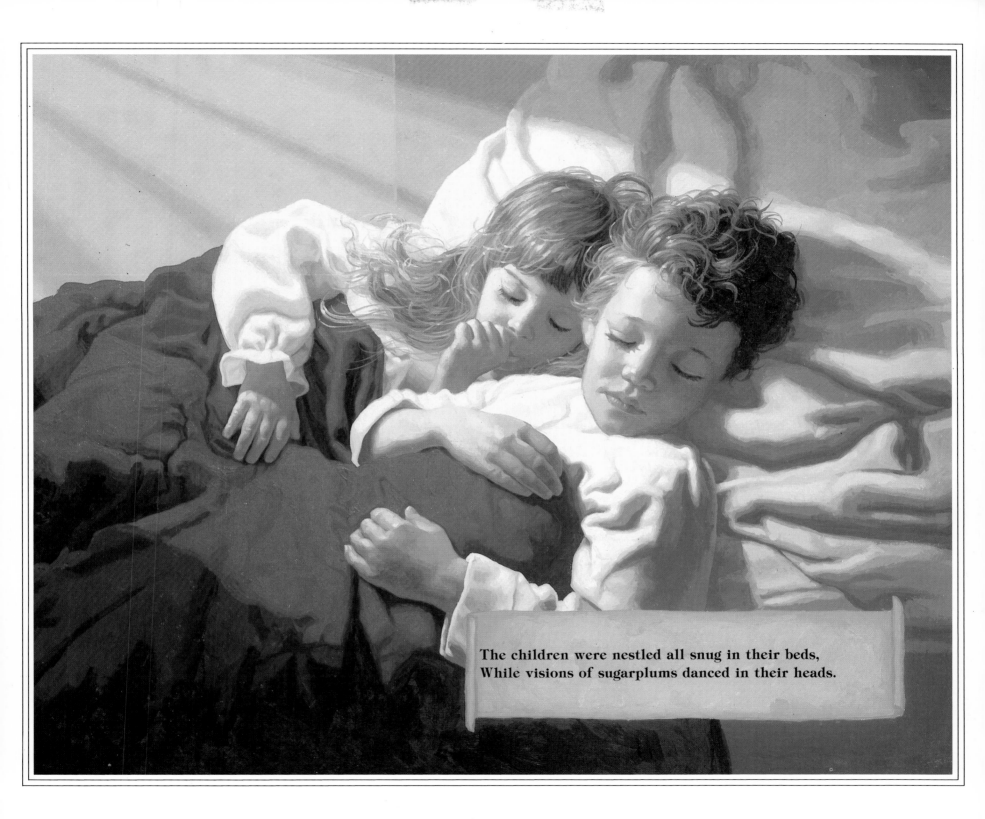

The children were nestled all snug in their beds,
While visions of sugarplums danced in their heads.

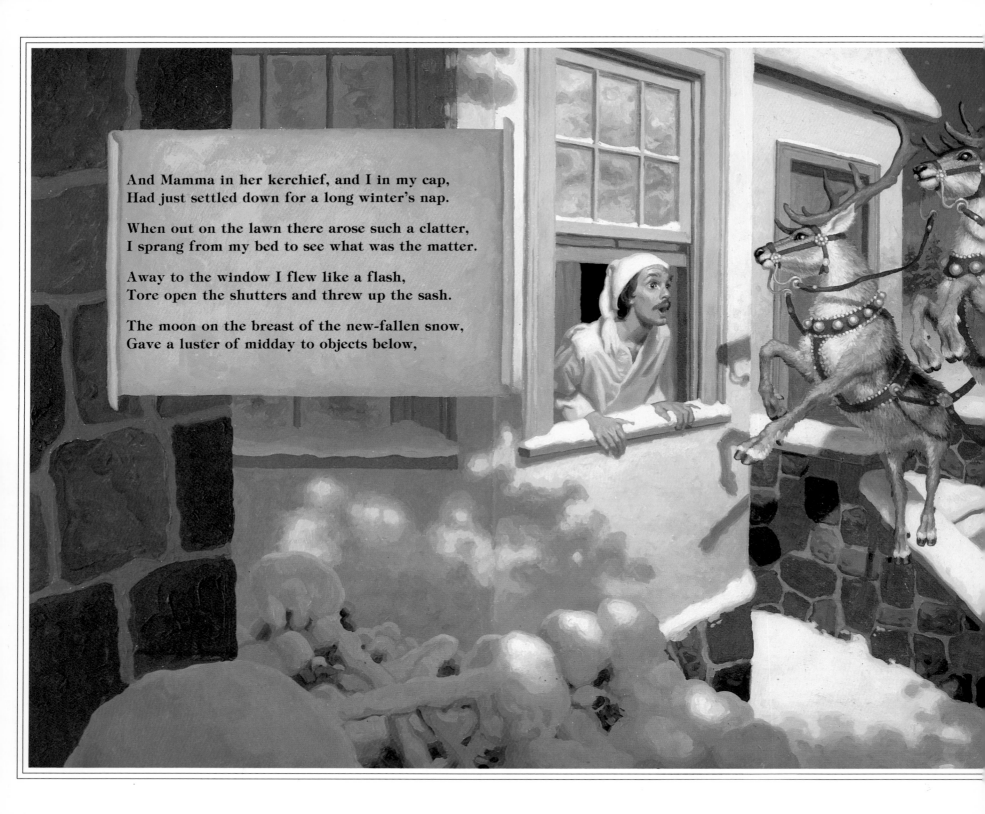

And Mamma in her kerchief, and I in my cap,
Had just settled down for a long winter's nap.

When out on the lawn there arose such a clatter,
I sprang from my bed to see what was the matter.

Away to the window I flew like a flash,
Tore open the shutters and threw up the sash.

The moon on the breast of the new-fallen snow,
Gave a luster of midday to objects below,

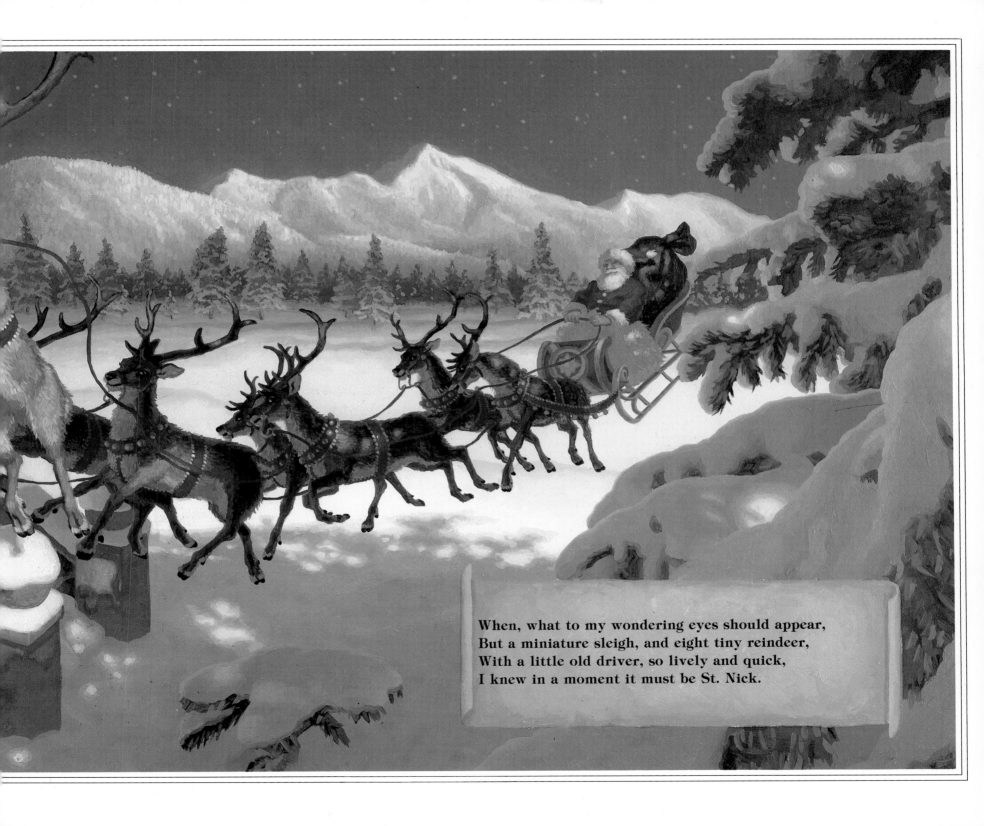

When, what to my wondering eyes should appear,
But a miniature sleigh, and eight tiny reindeer,
With a little old driver, so lively and quick,
I knew in a moment it must be St. Nick.

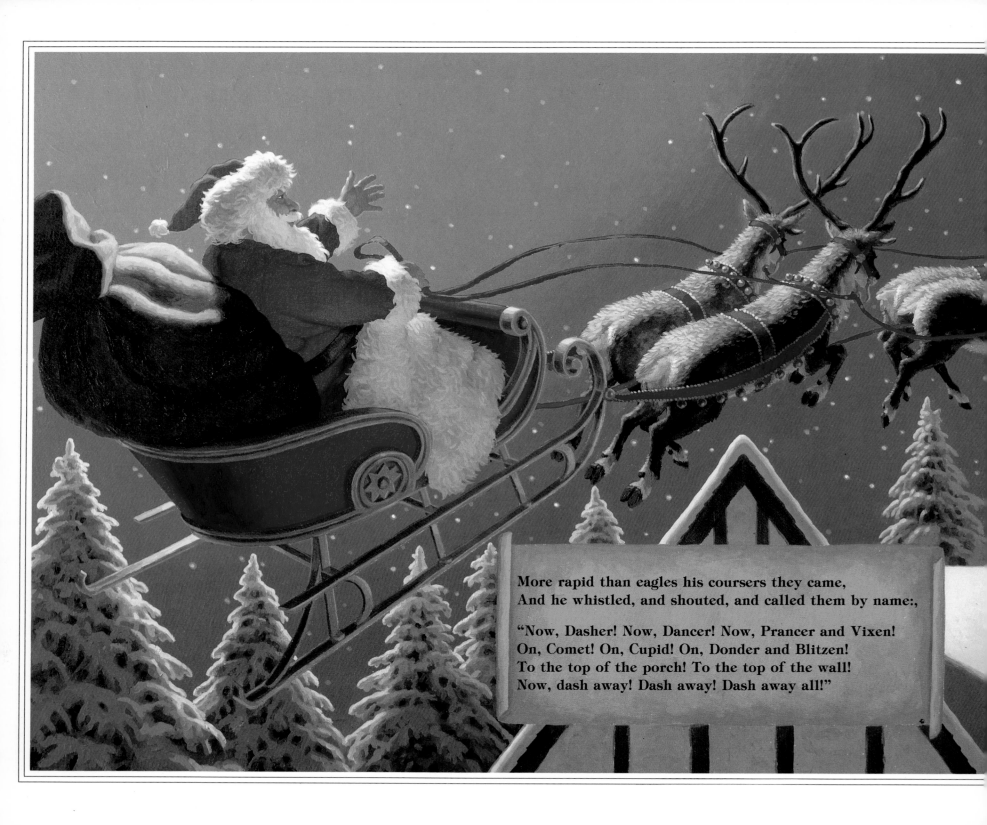

More rapid than eagles his coursers they came,
And he whistled, and shouted, and called them by name:,

"Now, Dasher! Now, Dancer! Now, Prancer and Vixen!
On, Comet! On, Cupid! On, Donder and Blitzen!
To the top of the porch! To the top of the wall!
Now, dash away! Dash away! Dash away all!"

As dry leaves that before the wild hurricane fly,
When they meet with an obstacle, mount to the sky,
So up to the housetop the coursers they flew,
With the sleigh full of toys, and St. Nicholas, too.

And then in a twinkling, I heard on the roof
The prancing and pawing of each little hoof.

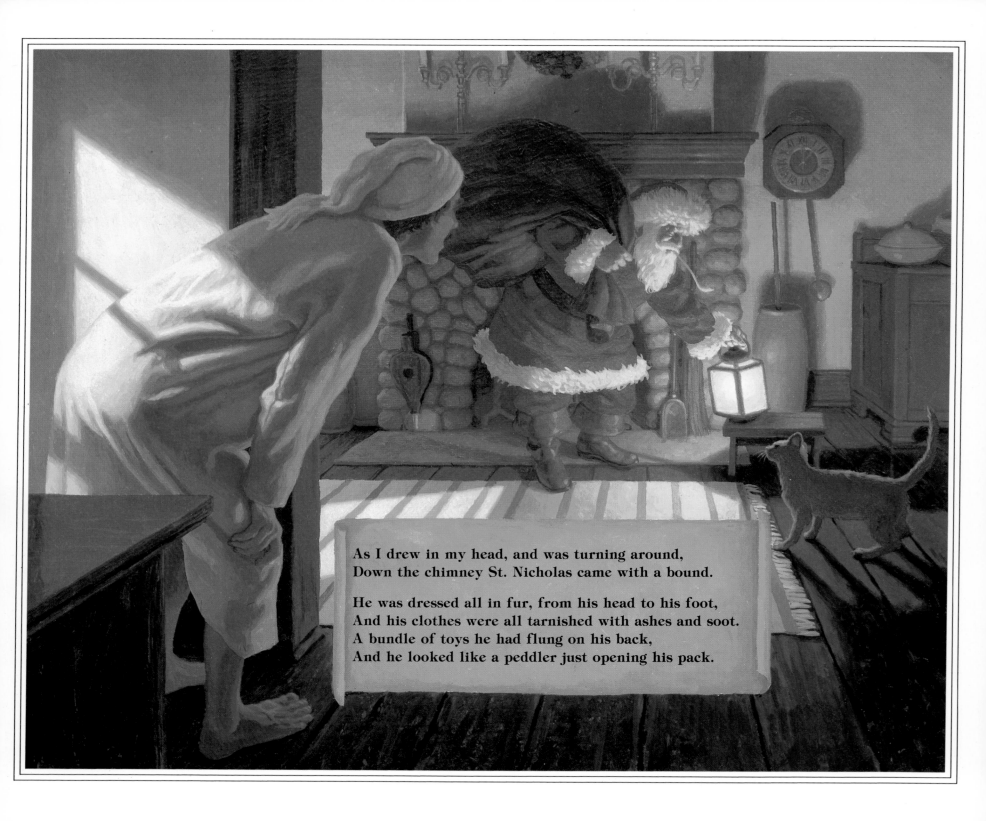

As I drew in my head, and was turning around,
Down the chimney St. Nicholas came with a bound.

He was dressed all in fur, from his head to his foot,
And his clothes were all tarnished with ashes and soot.
A bundle of toys he had flung on his back,
And he looked like a peddler just opening his pack.

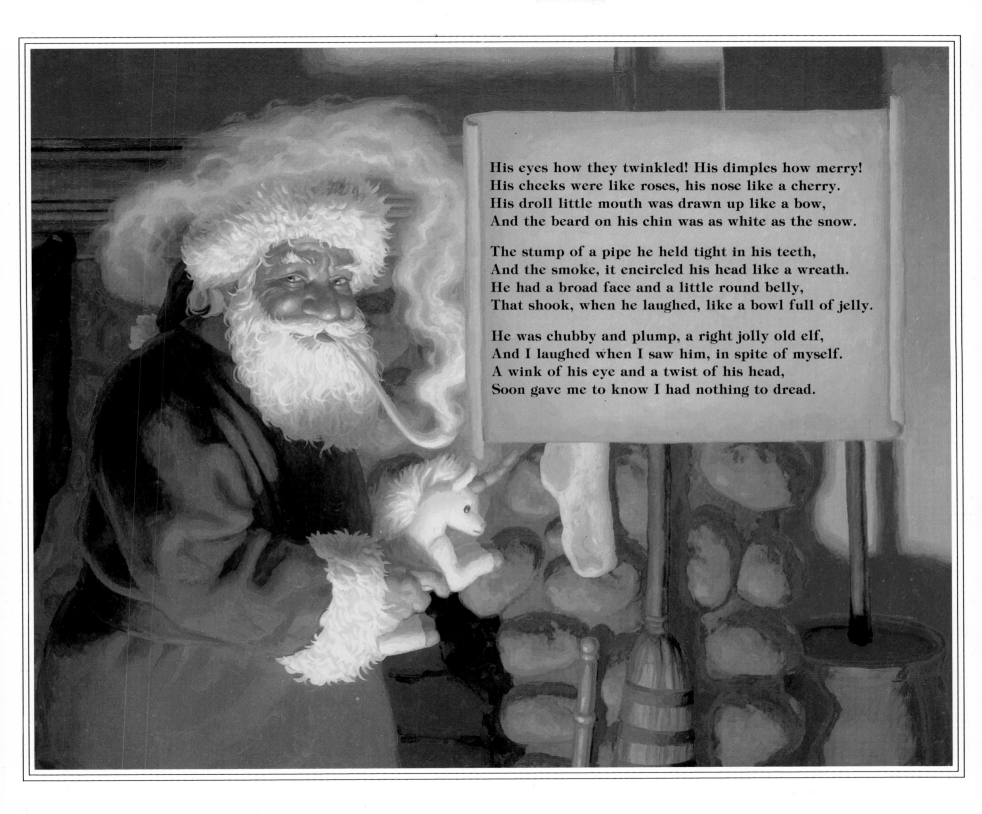

His eyes how they twinkled! His dimples how merry!
His cheeks were like roses, his nose like a cherry.
His droll little mouth was drawn up like a bow,
And the beard on his chin was as white as the snow.

The stump of a pipe he held tight in his teeth,
And the smoke, it encircled his head like a wreath.
He had a broad face and a little round belly,
That shook, when he laughed, like a bowl full of jelly.

He was chubby and plump, a right jolly old elf,
And I laughed when I saw him, in spite of myself.
A wink of his eye and a twist of his head,
Soon gave me to know I had nothing to dread.

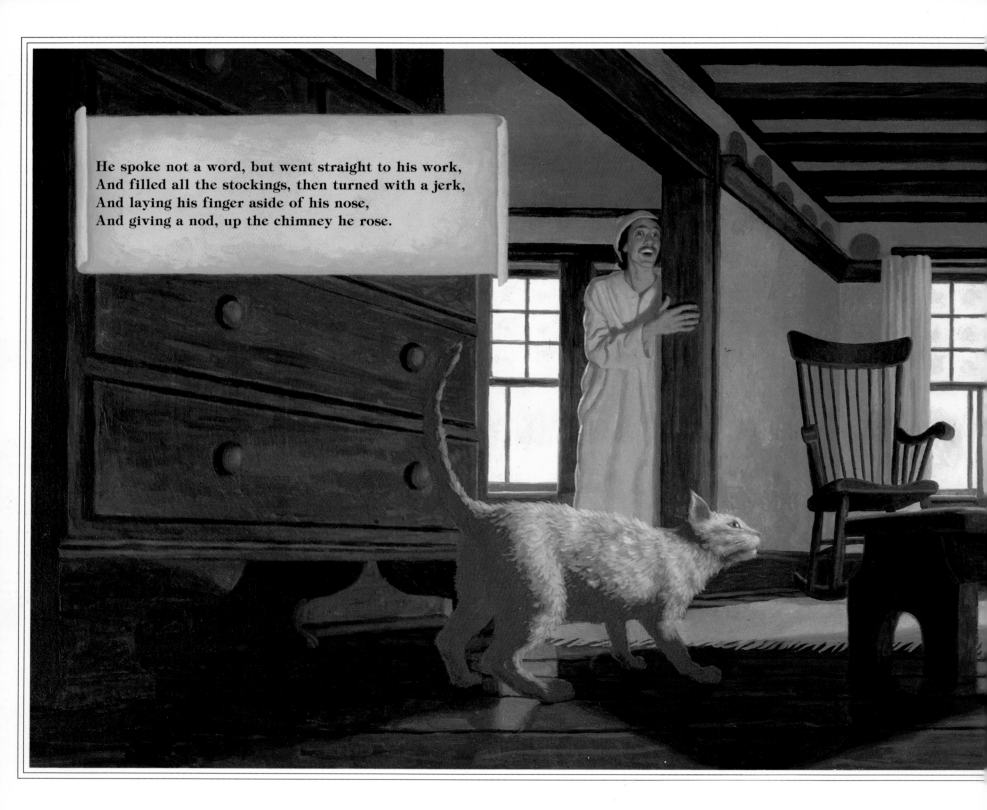

He spoke not a word, but went straight to his work,
And filled all the stockings, then turned with a jerk,
And laying his finger aside of his nose,
And giving a nod, up the chimney he rose.

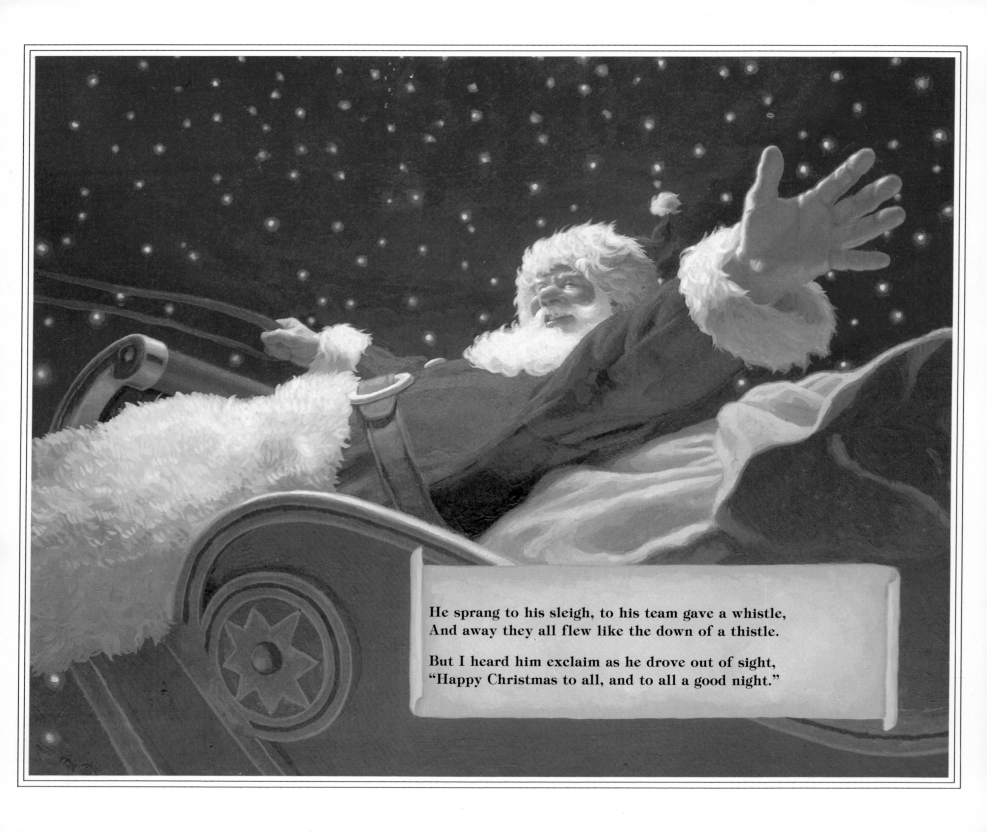

He sprang to his sleigh, to his team gave a whistle,
And away they all flew like the down of a thistle.

But I heard him exclaim as he drove out of sight,
"Happy Christmas to all, and to all a good night."

The Nativity of Jesus

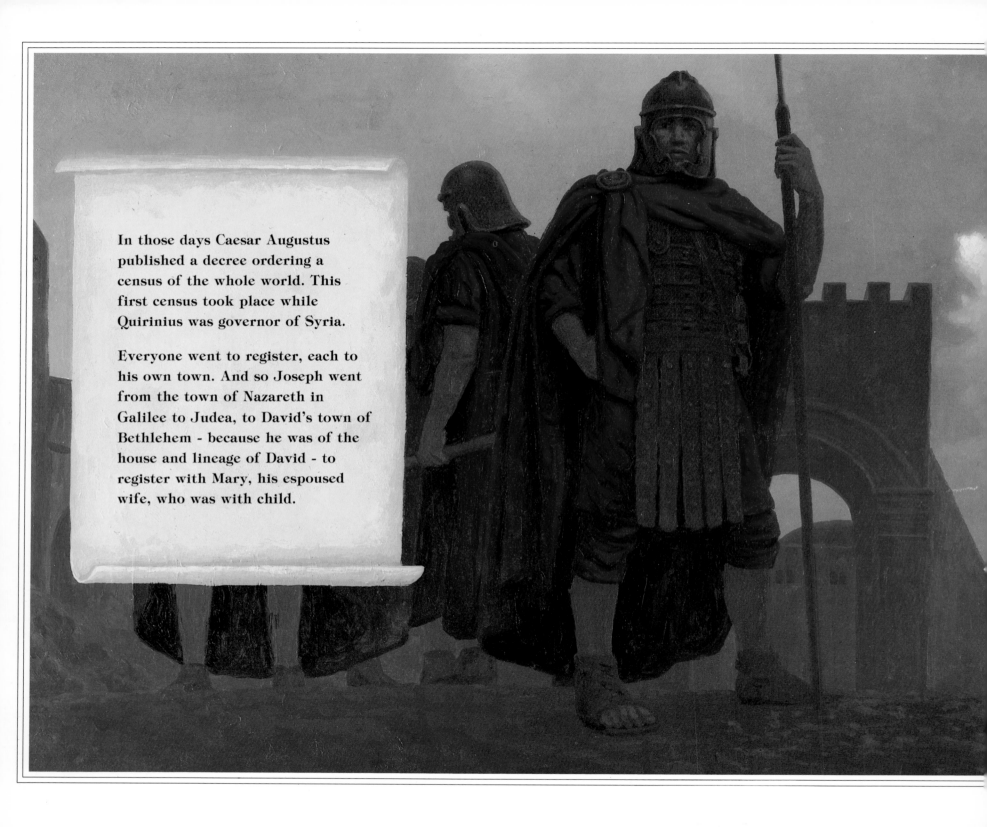

In those days Caesar Augustus published a decree ordering a census of the whole world. This first census took place while Quirinius was governor of Syria.

Everyone went to register, each to his own town. And so Joseph went from the town of Nazareth in Galilee to Judea, to David's town of Bethlehem - because he was of the house and lineage of David - to register with Mary, his espoused wife, who was with child.

While they were there the days of her confinement were completed.

She gave birth to her first-born son and wrapped him in swaddling clothes and laid him in a manger, because there was no room for them in the place where travelers lodged.

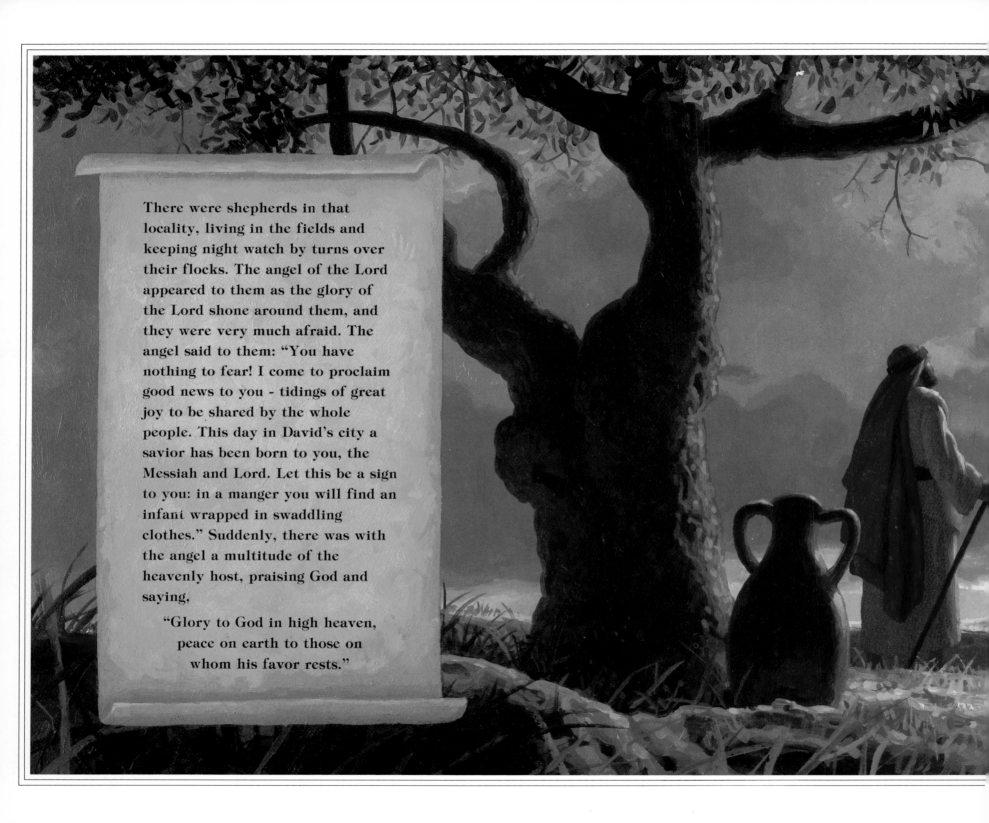

There were shepherds in that locality, living in the fields and keeping night watch by turns over their flocks. The angel of the Lord appeared to them as the glory of the Lord shone around them, and they were very much afraid. The angel said to them: "You have nothing to fear! I come to proclaim good news to you - tidings of great joy to be shared by the whole people. This day in David's city a savior has been born to you, the Messiah and Lord. Let this be a sign to you: in a manger you will find an infant wrapped in swaddling clothes." Suddenly, there was with the angel a multitude of the heavenly host, praising God and saying,

"Glory to God in high heaven, peace on earth to those on whom his favor rests."

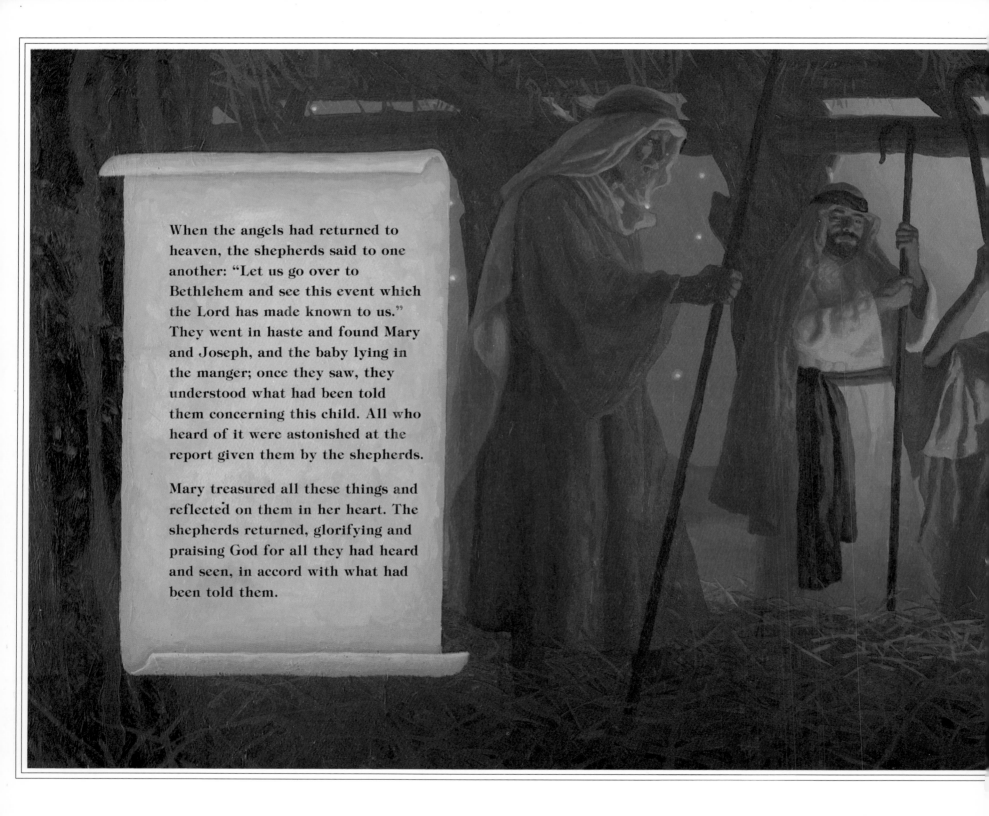

When the angels had returned to heaven, the shepherds said to one another: "Let us go over to Bethlehem and see this event which the Lord has made known to us." They went in haste and found Mary and Joseph, and the baby lying in the manger; once they saw, they understood what had been told them concerning this child. All who heard of it were astonished at the report given them by the shepherds.

Mary treasured all these things and reflected on them in her heart. The shepherds returned, glorifying and praising God for all they had heard and seen, in accord with what had been told them.

"Glory to God in high heaven,
peace on earth to those on
whom his favor rests."

Carols And Songs

Silent Night

Si - lent night, Ho - ly night, All is calm, all is bright.
Si - lent night, Ho - ly night, Shep - herds quake at the sight.
Si - lent night, Ho - ly night, Son of God, love's pure light.

'Round yon Vir - gin Moth - er and Child Ho - ly In - fant so ten - der and mild,
Glo - ries stream from heav - en a - far, Heav'n - ly hosts sing Al - le - lu - ia;
Ra - diant beams from Thy ho - ly face, With the dawn of re - deem - ing grace,

Sleep in heav - en - ly peace, _____ Sleep in heav - en - ly peace.
Christ the Sav - ior is born, _____ Christ the Sav - ior is born.
Je - sus, Lord, at Thy birth, _____ Je - sus, Lord, at Thy birth.

I Saw Three Ships

Deck The Halls

Jingle Bells

It Came Upon The Midnight Clear

It came up-on__ the mid-night clear, That glo-rious song__ of old,_____ From
Still through the clo - ven skies they come, With peace-ful wings__ un - furled;____ And
For lo! the days__ are hast - 'ning on, By proph-ets seen__ of old,_____ When

an - gels bend - ing near the earth, To touch their harps__ of gold:_____ "Peace
still their heav'n - ly mu - sic floats O'er all the wea - ry world;____ A -
with the ev - er - cir - cling years, Shall come the time__ fore - told,_____ When

on the earth,__ good will to men, From heaven's__ all gra - cious King."____ The
bove its sad__ and lone - ly plains, They bend__ on hov - er - ing wing,____ And
the new heaven__ and earth shall own The Prince__ of Peace__ their King,____ And

world in sol - emn still - ness lay To hear the an - gels sing. _____
ev - er o'er__ its Ba - bel sounds The bless - ed an - gels sing. _____
the whole world__ send back the song Which now the an - gels sing. _____

O Christmas Tree

We Three Kings

We three kings of O - ri - ent are; Bear - ing gifts we trav - erse a -
Born a King on Beth - le - hem plain, Gold we bring to crown Him a -

far, Field and foun - tain, moor and moun - tain, Fol - low - ing yon - der star.
gain, King for - ev - er, ceas - ing nev - er O - ver us all to reign.

O, _____ star of won - der, star of night, Star with roy - al beau - ty bright;

West - ward lead - ing, still pro - ceed - ing, Guide us to Thy per - fect light.

Twelve Days of Christmas

On the first day of Christmas my true love sent to me
A partridge in a pear tree.

On the second day of Christmas my true love sent to me
Two turtle doves and a partridge in a pear tree.

On the third day of Christmas my true love sent to me
Three French hens,
Two turtle doves and a partridge in a pear tree.

On the fourth day of Christmas my true love sent to me
Four cawing birds, three French hens,
Two turtle doves and a partridge in a pear tree.

On the fifth day of Christmas my true love sent to me
Five gold rings!
Four cawing birds, three French hens,
Two turtle doves and a partridge in a pear tree.

On the sixth day of Christmas my true love sent to me
Six geese a-laying,
Five gold rings!
Four cawing birds, three French hens,
Two turtle doves and a partridge in a pear tree.

On the seventh day of Christmas my true love sent to me
Seven swans a-swimming, six geese a-laying,
Five gold rings!
Four cawing birds, three French hens,
Two turtle doves and a partridge in a pear tree.

On the eighth day of Christmas my true love sent to me
Eight maids a-milking,
Seven swans a-swimming, six geese a-laying,
Five gold rings!
Four cawing birds, three French hens,
Two turtle doves and a partridge in a pear tree.

On the ninth day of Christmas my true love sent to me
Nine ladies dancing, eight maids a-milking,
Seven swans a-swimming, six geese a-laying,
Five gold rings!
Four cawing birds, three French hens,
Two turtle doves and a partridge in a pear tree.

On the tenth day of Christmas my true love sent to me
Ten lords a-leaping,
Nine ladies dancing, eight maids a-milking,
Seven swans a-swimming, six geese a-laying,
Five gold rings!
Four cawing birds, three French hens,
Two turtle doves and a partridge in a pear tree.

On the eleventh day of Christmas my true love sent to me
Eleven pipers piping, ten lords a-leaping,
Nine ladies dancing, eight maids a-milking,
Seven swans a-swimming, six geese a-laying,
Five gold rings!
Four cawing birds, three French hens,
Two turtle doves and a partridge in a pear tree.

On the twelfth day of Christmas my true love sent to me
Twelve drummers drumming,
Eleven pipers piping, ten lords a-leaping,
Nine ladies dancing, eight maids a-milking,
Seven swans a-swimming, six geese a-laying,
Five gold rings!
Four cawing birds, three French hens,
Two turtle doves,
And a partridge in a pear tree!

Additional Classic and Contemporary Editions
Richly Illustrated by Greg Hildebrandt,

THE WIZARD OF OZ
DRACULA
FROM TOLKIEN TO OZ
PETER COTTONTAIL'S SURPRISE
GREG HILDEBRANDT'S FAVORITE FAIRY TALES
A CHRISTMAS CAROL

First published in 1997
This edition published 2000
by Franklin Watts
96 Leonard Street,
London EC2A 4XD

Franklin Watts Australia
14 Mars Road
Lane Cove
NSW 2066

Text copyright
© Pippa Goodhart 1997, 2000
Illustrations copyright
© Brita Granström 1997, 2000

Series editor: Paula Borton
Art director: Robert Walster

Photography Steve Shott
With thanks to Ben Ridley-Johnson

A CIP catalogue record for this
book is available from the British
Library.

ISBN 0 7496 2718 2 (hbk)
ISBN 0 7496 3489 8 (pbk)

Dewey Classification 398.23

Printed in Belgium

Consultant advice: Sue Robson and Alison Kelly, Senior Lecturers in Education,
Faculty of Education, Early Childhood Centre, Roehampton Institute, London.

Paperback titles in this series:

Pets	Weather	Who are you?	Time	First Experiences
Guinea Pig	Windy day	In the Sea	Morning time	New shoes
0 7496 3498 7	0 7496 3497 9	0 7496 3510 X	0 7496 3487 1	0 7496 3492 8
Kitten	Snowy day	In the Polar Lands	Play time	A party
0 7496 3499 5	0 7496 3495 2	0 7496 3511 8	0 7496 3488 X	0 7496 3491 X
Puppy	Sunny day	On the Farm	Shopping time	Staying the night
0 7496 3500 2	0 7496 3496 0	0 7496 3512 6	0 7496 3489 8	0 7496 3490 1
Rabbit	Rainy day	In the Rainforest	Bed time	Big bed
0 7496 3501 0	0 7496 3494 4	0 7496 3513 4	0 7496 3486 3	0 7496 3493 6

For Polly – PG